WHERE'S WALLY?
THE COLOURING COLLECTION
MARTIN HANDFORD

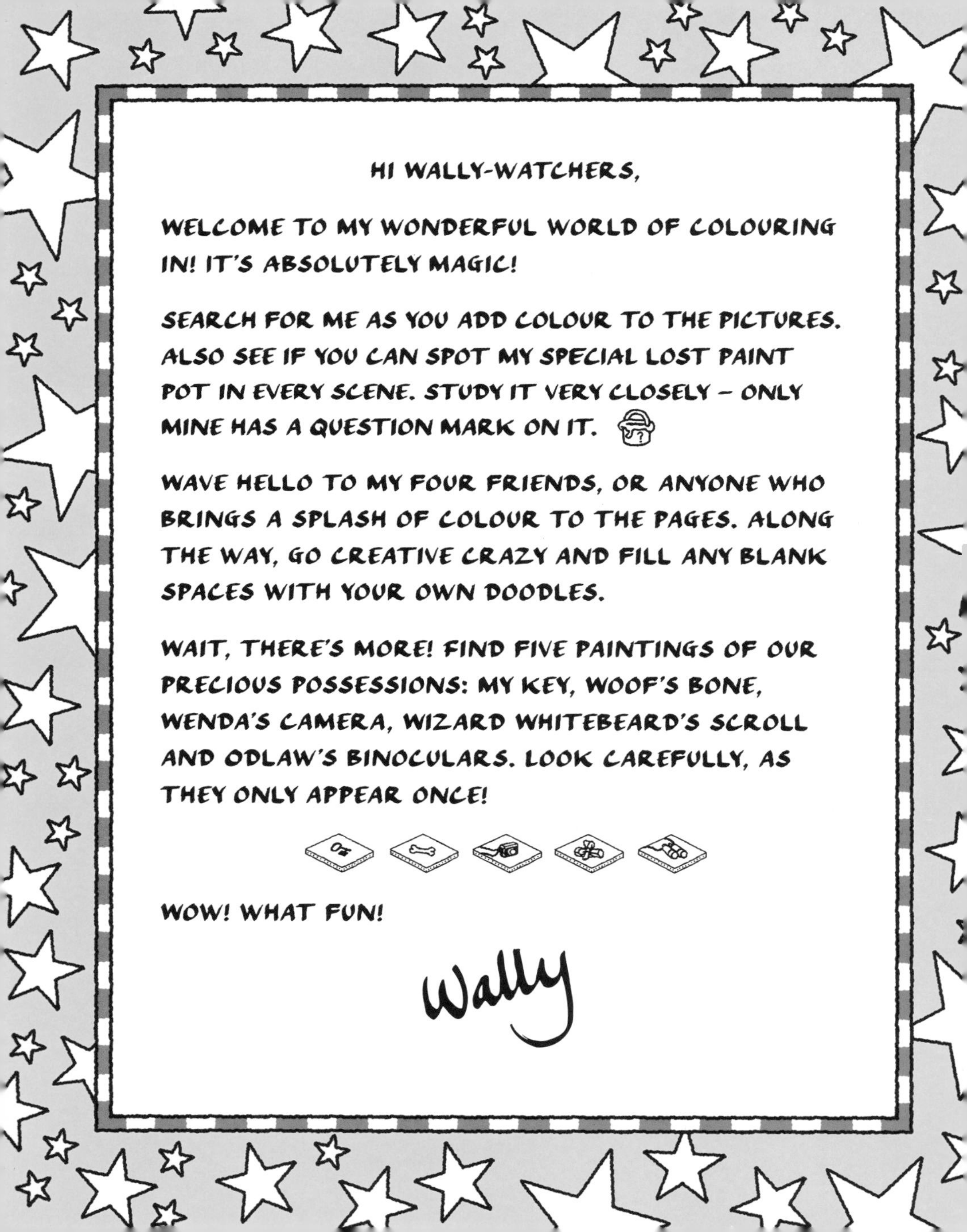

HI WALLY-WATCHERS,

WELCOME TO MY WONDERFUL WORLD OF COLOURING IN! IT'S ABSOLUTELY MAGIC!

SEARCH FOR ME AS YOU ADD COLOUR TO THE PICTURES. ALSO SEE IF YOU CAN SPOT MY SPECIAL LOST PAINT POT IN EVERY SCENE. STUDY IT VERY CLOSELY – ONLY MINE HAS A QUESTION MARK ON IT.

WAVE HELLO TO MY FOUR FRIENDS, OR ANYONE WHO BRINGS A SPLASH OF COLOUR TO THE PAGES. ALONG THE WAY, GO CREATIVE CRAZY AND FILL ANY BLANK SPACES WITH YOUR OWN DOODLES.

WAIT, THERE'S MORE! FIND FIVE PAINTINGS OF OUR PRECIOUS POSSESSIONS: MY KEY, WOOF'S BONE, WENDA'S CAMERA, WIZARD WHITEBEARD'S SCROLL AND ODLAW'S BINOCULARS. LOOK CAREFULLY, AS THEY ONLY APPEAR ONCE!

WOW! WHAT FUN!

Wally

WIZARD WHITEBEARD
WALLY
ODLAW
WENDA
WOOF

WHERE'S
WALLY?

DRAW EYES, NOSES AND MOUTHS TO FINISH
SOME FACES IN MY STAMP COLLECTION!

HOW MANY WOOFS CAN YOU COUNT AND COLOUR IN?

CAN YOU ALSO SPOT A SHARK FIN? YIKES!

THINK UP TITLES FOR THESE BOOKS AND DRAW THEM IN!

ADD DINOSAUR DRAWINGS TO
WOOF'S TWO UNFINISHED DOG
TAGS. BOW-WOW! ROAR!

SPIN SIDEWAYS AND MAKE YOUR WAY TO THE TOP OF THE LIGHTHOUSE WITH COLOUR!

ALOON
MONTANA
OKLA
TEXAS
THE ROCKIES
THE MID WEST
COLORADO
MONTANA
OKLAHOMA
DODGE CITY
TEXAS

DODGE CITY
TEXAS

ENTER, IF YOU DARE! IT'S SUPER SPOOKY!

WENDA LOVES TAKING PICTURES WITH
HER CAMERA. BRING COLOUR TO HER FUN
PHOTOS AND FILL THEM WITH PEOPLE!

WHAT AMAZING LUNCHES EVERYONE IS HAVING HERE!

HOW MANY TRAYS OF FOOD CAN YOU FIND AND COLOUR?

LIGHTS, CAMERA, ACTION ... COLOUR!

THERE'S LOTS OF HULLABALLOO IN HOLLYWOOD!

IT'S TIME TO GET CREATIVE AND FILL THESE FRAMES WITH ART OF YOUR OWN!

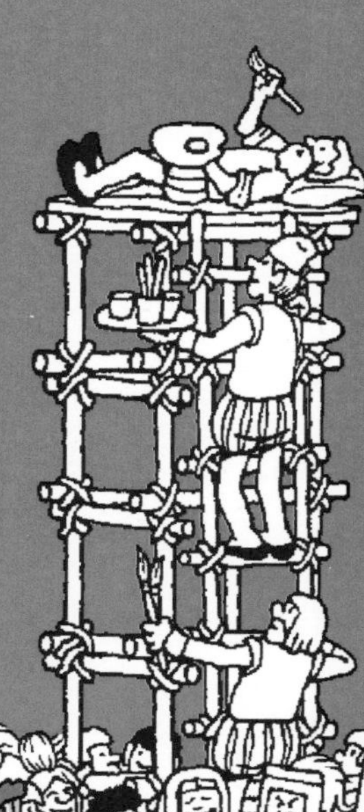

IMAGINE TITLES FOR THESE GREAT BOOKS!

MAKE NEW THINGS APPEAR IN THE BLANK SPACES OF WIZARD WHITEBEARD'S SPELL BOOK COVERS!

WHAT CAN YOU "SEA"? HA, HA!

SEARCH AND COLOUR! AHOY!

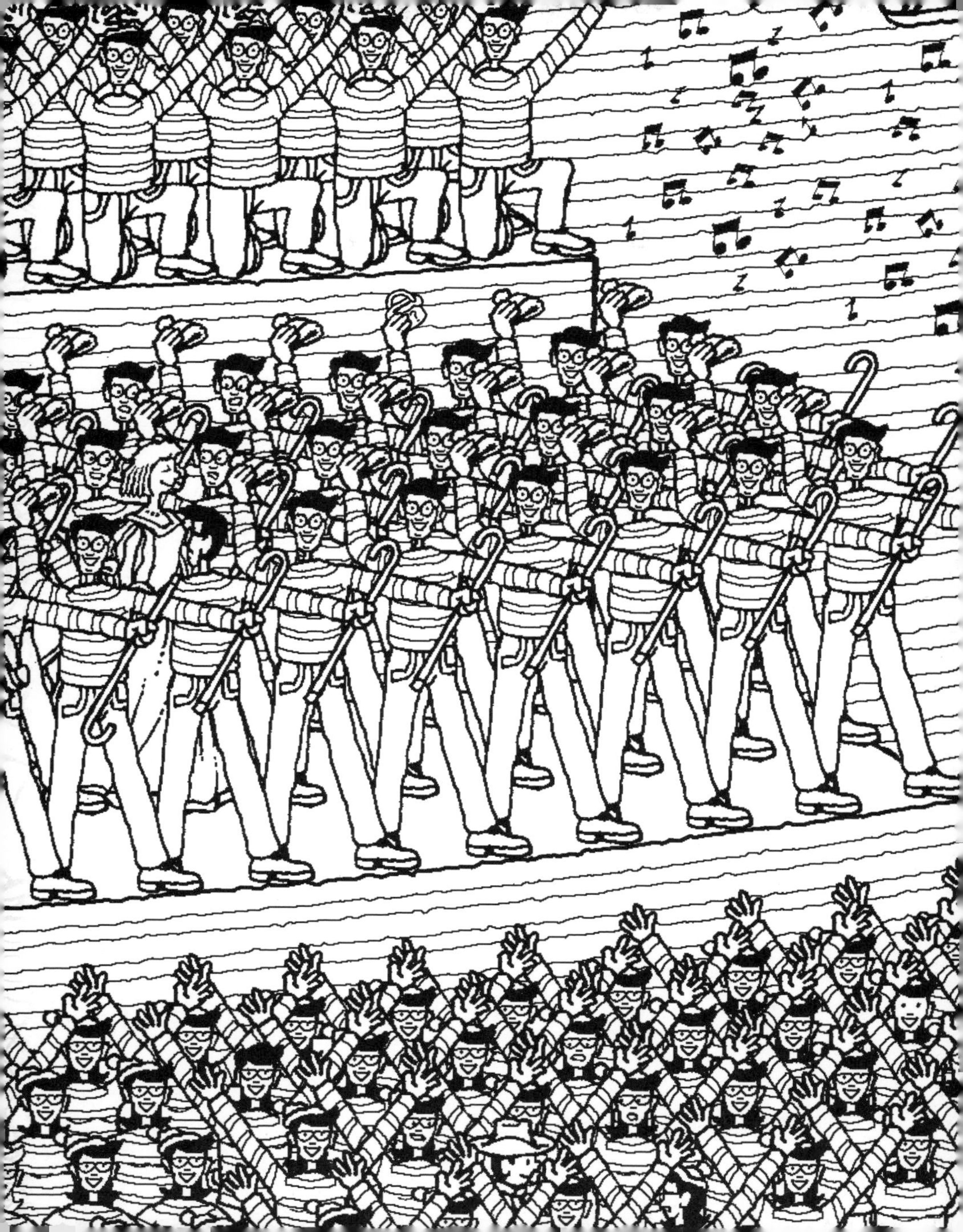

COLOUR IN THIS DRAGON DELIGHT!

CAN YOU FIND A CURLY DRAGON TAIL?

SPY THROUGH ODLAW'S BINOCULARS
TO SPOT SUPER SNEAKY VILLAINS!

SEARCH FOR TWO HIDING VILLAINS!

WHAT COLOURFUL CHAOS! WOW!

WHAT A COLOUR CRAZY ADVENTURE WITH ME AND MY FRIENDS!

WE HOPE YOU HAD FUN! FIND THE CHECKLISTS OVER THE PAGE.

WHERE'S WALLY?
An astronaut
A flower in a woman's hair
An alien
An apple hat
Four clown noses
A person with a sad expression
A trumpet
Two toy rhinoceros
Two crowns
A pair of swimming trunks
A watch dog
A Woof wearing flippers
A man looking in a mirror
A celebrity wearing a new dress
A big bow tie
A one pence stamp
A female scientist
A very tall top hat

The numbers three and six
Two pterodactyls holding golf clubs
Two snoozing dinosaurs
Two rock crowns
A dinosaur hit by the tail of another
Twenty dog tags
A player painting a dice
A player throwing a six
A map reading
An upside down dragon
A shared telescope
A light weight boxer
A flower water feature
Uprooted flowers
Flower beds
A snaky question mark
A ponytail paintbrush
A sword

A couple of gunslingers
An umbrella
A bag of loot
Five stars
Two mummies
Someone trapped in a tree
A dizzy clown
An extra large egg
Cards playing cards
Two mixing desks
Drainpipe trousers
Two bugs jitterbugging
Frankenstein
A robot
A woman looking at her watch
Two flags
Bandsmen reading newspapers
Three drummers with carrot sticks

HOLLYWOOD
Someone waving a handkerchief
A bird costume
A rabbit costume
A guitarist
A handbag
An axe with teeth through it
The Invisible Man
A beanstalk
A man playing a harmonica
Horses wearing ear muffs
Six soldiers covering their ears
Two hats joined together
An empty chair
A Wizard Whitebeard with glasses
An upset dragon and rider
Two pirate hats with only a skull
A bejewelled cauldron
A snake

Two three-eyed aliens
An alien with four eyes
A space ship
A ticklish apple
An apple being tripped up
An apple being clubbed by a lemon
A caged sea monster
A floating light bulb
A bed
A Wally without jean pockets
A Wenda without glasses
A cowboy
Two dragons and their riders in love
Two dragon riders riding backwards
Two bobble hats
A Viking
Two people pulling a rope
Someone wearing sunglasses